THE
BUTTERFLIES OF KENT

an atlas of their distribution

by

Eric G. Philp

Transactions of the Kent Field Club

Volume 12

Sittingbourne 1993

KENT FIELD CLUB

AIMS

To promote an increased interest in Natural History,
to study and record the distribution
and ecology of the fauna and flora,
and to promote nature conservation
in association with the relevant organisations,
within the County of Kent.

CONTENTS

THE BUTTERFLIES OF KENT

by Eric G Philp

INTRODUCTION

From 1971 onwards Maidstone Museum has run a Kent Biological Archives and Records Centre in which records of all plants and animals found in the county are kept. Whilst published records and details of special studies or counts are included, the bulk of the records entered into these Archives are of distribution records based on the tetrad grid system. A tetrad is a unit of land two kilometres by two kilometres as defined by the even numbered grid lines found on the Ordnance Survey maps. In the present county of Kent there are 1042 tetrads, although those around the edges are not full size, as part of the tetrad comprises sea or part of an adjoining county. For the purposes of the Kent Biological Archives an attempt has been made to obtain one dated record of each species of butterfly that occurs in each tetrad each year and this policy will continue. From these records it is hoped to be able in the future to plot long term expansion or contraction in the range and distribution of our butterflies.

The most detailed and comprehensive account of the butterflies of the county is to be found in *The Butterflies and Moths of Kent* by J.M. Chalmers-Hunt which was published as supplements in The Entomologist's Record and Journal of Variation over the years 1968 to 1981. This publication is now out of print and difficult to obtain and, with a growing interest in the butterflies of our countryside, it was felt that there was a demand for a quick reference to the present state of the butterflies in the county. So, backed by the Kent Field Club, it was decided to put in a special effort over the years 1981 to 1990 inclusive to record the distribution of the butterflies of Kent and to publish the results. This booklet is the result of this effort.

Records of butterflies observed in the county from 1981 to 1990 were sent to the author at Maidstone Museum where they were checked and then entered into the Kent Biological Archives. Because of the limited flying season of many species and with the restriction of flying days by the weather, the size of the task soon became apparent and help was solicited from as many organisations and persons as possible. Even then there was a tendency for recorders to concentrate on the 'honey-pot' areas such as the Downs at Shoreham and Kemsing, Holly Hill, Darland Banks, Wye and Crundale Downs, Orlestone Forest, Denge Wood, the Blean Woods, Temple Ewell and the coastal chalk area between Folkestone, Dover and Deal. So, towards the end of the ten years, recorders were urged to take a large block of land under their wing, preferably a ten kilometre square, and record over the whole area so as to get a more even coverage. Even then not all the county was covered and the writer attempted to fill in the uncovered areas. Recording butterflies in some of the 'poorer' areas of farmland or coastal marsh can often be quite hard work, entailing many miles of walking, and then perhaps when spotting the first White butterfly of the day it is the other side of a dyke and cannot be identified down to species. Thanks are due to all the recorders who helped compile these records and their names are listed at the end of this chapter.

Map 1 shows the coverage achieved during this survey with tetrads indicated according to whether 1 - 10, 11 - 20 or more than 21 species were recorded. Of the 1042 tetrads only 23 had no records and these were mainly part tetrads around the edges of the county. It had been hoped to record at least 11 species of butterfly from every tetrad but this was not achieved partly through lack of man-power and partly because in some of the heavily farmed areas that lack any woodland or chalk downland then the variety of species of butterfly is just not found. However, in 123 tetrads (nearly 12%) 21 or more species were recorded, and these richer areas can be picked out on the map, particularly where they are concentrated. The most species-rich tetrads were the Faggs Wood-Longrope Wood area of Orlestone Forest TQ93X with 32 species, the Downs between Lydden - Temple Ewell TR24S with 31 species, and Kemsing Down TQ55P, Wye Downs TR04S and Folkestone Warren TR23N each with 30 species.

Map 2 shows the general outline of the county together with the major towns and built-up areas shaded in. Increasing urbanisation in the west of the county has led to the loss of a number of suitable breeding sites for butterflies and a general decline in butterfly richness in these areas as a consequence.

2

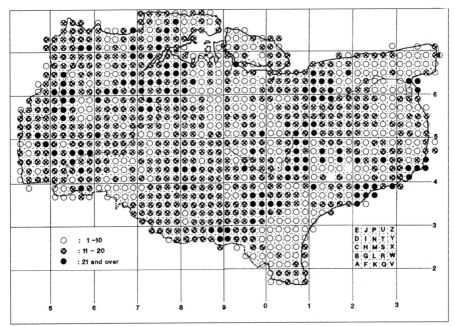

Map 1. Number of butterfly species per tetrad

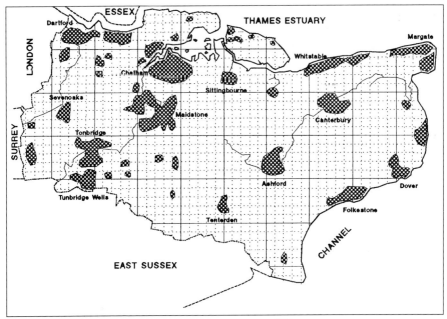

Map 2. Urban areas of Kent

3

LIST OF CONTRIBUTORS

The following people have contributed records to this Atlas, some with several hundred records regularly each year, others with records at irregular intervals and some with only perhaps a single record, but without whose help the production of the distribution maps would not have been possible. I must particularly thank Mr. Peter Heathcote for his help in preparing the maps for publication and Mrs Gill Brook for the beautiful line drawings. Photographs were supplied by Mrs Gill Brook and Mr Michael Enfield.

Adams, K. & M.	Dodds, B.	Huxley, M.P.
Allen, G.W.	Doe, B.	
Ambrose, B.	Dolling, M.H.	Ironside, K.
	Dominey, D.	
Badmin, J. S. & J.A.	Dykes, D.O.	Jenner, D.
Banner, C.		Jenner, M.
Barber, A.D.	Easterbrook, M.	Jennings, M.T.
Barnes, B.	Ely, W.A.	Jervis, J.S.
Beavis, I.	Enfield, M.	Jewess, P.J.
Bindon, C.	Evans, A.	Johnson, C.
Blackman, A.	Eve, H.C.	
Blagden, A.J.		Kesby, J.
Bland, P.	Ferguson, I.D.	Kitchener, G.N.
Bond, R.D.M.	Flegg, J.J.M.	
Booth, F.	Flint, T.	Langton, J.
Bradford, E.S.	Fray, A.E.	Lewis, I.T.
Brook, J. & G.	Frazer, J.F.D.	Lloyd, D.F.
Brown, M.R.		Lock, C.
Burn, J.	Garrett, H.	Lodge, K.
	Gay, P.H.	Lynes, H.
Carpenter, T.	Gnomes, B.	
Carter, D.B.	Gossling, N.F.	Mallett, P.L.V.
Chambers, D.	Greenwood, P.C.	Matthews, N.
Chatfield, B.G.	Grimes, B.	McAllister, J.
Clancy, S.		McLaren, J.
Clemons, L.	Harman, T.	Measday, A.V.
Clinber, T.J.	Harvey, R.	Memory, V.
Cobbald, J.	Heal, N.R.	Moreton, B.D.
Cooper, A.	Heathcote, P.C. & P.	Mussellwhite, A. & B.
Coultrup, W.	Heaton, A.	
Crow, M.	Henderson, A.	Newcombe, M.
Cummings, D.	Highwood, S.	
Cwynerski, M.	Hodge, P.J.	Onslow, N.
	Hogg, P.	Orsbourne, C.
Davis, G.A.N.	Hollis, J.	Ottley, A.
Davis, O.	Horton, P.	
Derrett, K.	Howell, A.D.	Page, M.

4

Palmer, K.
Parker, S.J.
Pattock, R.J.
Peacock, A.
Penney, D. & M.
Percival, M.
Petley-Jones, R.
Petty, A.G.
Philcox, S.
Philp, E.G.
Pink, P.
Pitt, J.
Plant, C.W.
Platts, J.
Potts, R.
Puckett, J.

Redgrave, A.C.
Richards, D.

Rigg, A.
Riley, P.
Robbins, J.
Roberts, P.
Rollins, C.C.
Ruck, T.
Rundle, A.J.
Russell, J.

Samson, C.
Side, A.G.
Stanyon, C.
Steele, A.
Still, E.C.
Stone, R.C.
Strickland, L.
Stringer, J.

Taplin, J.

Taylor, R.E.
Thompsett, K.
Tickner, M.
Trollope, C.E.
Tutt, D.

Waite, M.
Warren, E.J.M.
Warry, S.
Waters, K.
White, R. & P.
Whitebread, R.
Whiteley, D.
Wignell, T.
Willard. C.
Williams, S.A.
Woodcock, M.

Youden, G.A.

REFERENCES

Chalmers-Hunt, J.M., (1960-1961) . *The Butterflies and Moths of Kent: A Critical Account*. Part 1: *Introduction and Rhopalocera*. West Wickham. (Originally published as supplements to *Entomologist's Rec. J. Var.* 72-73).

Chalmers-Hunt, J.M., (1968-1981) . *The Butterflies and Moths of Kent*. Volume 3: *Heterocera and Supplement*. West Wickham, (Originally published as supplements to *Entomologist's Rec. J. Var.* 80-93.

Emmet, A.M., et al, (1989) . *The Moths and Butterflies of Great Britain and Ireland*, Vol. 7, Part 1, *The Butterflies*. Harley Books.

Firmin, J., et al, (1975) . *A Guide to the butterflies and larger moths of Essex*. Fingringhoe: Essex Naturalists' Trust.

Goss, H. & Barrett, C.G., (1908). Lepidoptera. *Victoria County History* 1: 178-208.

Philp, E.G., (1982). *Atlas of the Kent Flora*. Kent Field Club.

Plant, C.W., (1987) . *The Butterflies of the London Area*. London Natural History Society.

Scott, E., (1964) . Annotated List of Lepidoptera occurring in the neighbourhood of Ashford, Kent. *Trans. Kent Field Club*, Vol. 2.

SPECIES ACCOUNT

Butterflies occur throughout Kent, the species and numbers depending upon the time of year and the habitat. On warm days from February onwards one is likely to find Small Tortoiseshells or Brimstones flying, the former just about anywhere in the county, the Brimstone much less frequent or absent from some of the coastal areas. As the days get longer and warmer then more species steadily put in an appearance, with different species peaking in numbers at different times of the summer.

Some of the best places to see butterflies are the well-wooded areas in the Weald such as in the Orlestone Forest south of Ashford, in the Blean Woods near Canterbury (Map 3), or in chalk downland areas near Shoreham or Wye (Map 4). By September the numbers of butterflies start decreasing but species such as the Small Copper, Red Admiral or Speckled Wood will still be on the wing until the end of October or even later. The winter months of December and January are usually very quiet for butterflies with perhaps just an occasional straggler lingering on from the summer or a hibernator disturbed from its winter rest.

The following account lists all the species of butterfly recorded in the county with a brief note on status, food plants and flight periods. The accompanying distribution maps show where each species was recorded from 1981 - 1990 inclusive and although not claiming to be exhaustive, each map does give a good idea of where each species is likely to be found in the county.

In the *Atlas of the Kent Flora* (Philp, 1982) will be found tetrad maps showing the distribution of the various larval food plants of the butterflies found within the county.

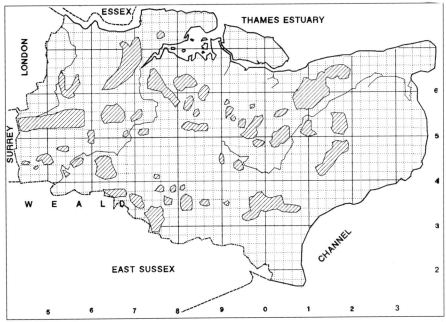

Map 3. Main wooded areas of Kent

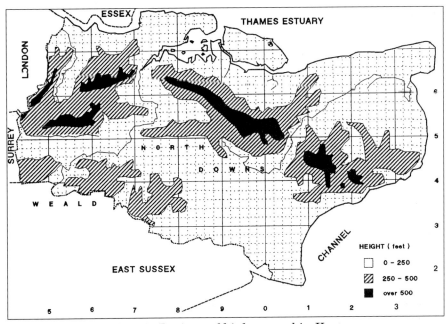

HEIGHT (feet)

☐ 0 – 250
▨ 250 – 500
■ over 500

Map 4. Regions of high ground in Kent

7

SMALL SKIPPER *Thymelicus sylvestris* (Poda)

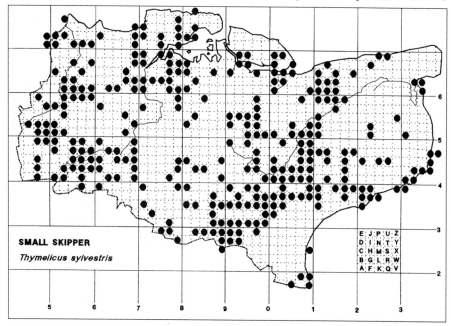

SMALL SKIPPER
Thymelicus sylvestris

Native. Scattered colonies throughout the county in areas of rough grassland as found on roadside verges, open downland and woodland rides and edges. It does not occur in grassland areas that are regularly cut nor in thickly wooded or heavily built-up areas.

The larvae, which over-winter in their first instar, have been observed feeding upon Yorkshire-fog *Holcus lanatus*, Creeping Soft-grass *Holcus mollis*, Timothy *Phleum pratense* and False Brome *Brachypodium sylvaticum*. The adults are on the wing in July and early August, the extreme dates noted during this survey being 18th June and 29th August. Almost certainly not as common as formerly and perhaps a little over-recorded in mistake for the following species.

ESSEX SKIPPER   *Thymelicus lineola* (Ochsenheimer)

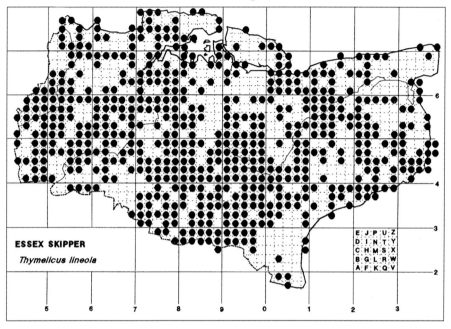

ESSEX SKIPPER
Thymelicus lineola

Native. First recorded in Kent in 1891 some two years after its discovery as a British insect in Essex. It is now found throughout the county in coastal marshes, woodland rides and borders, roadside verges and other rough grassy areas. Having overwintered as an egg, the resultant larvae feed up on grasses in the early summer. Yorkshire-fog *Holcus lanatus* is the only host so far positively recorded in the county but other species of grass are probably eaten as well. The majority of the adults are on the wing during the last two weeks in July and the first three weeks in August with the extreme dates of 29th June and 2nd September. Frequent throughout the county and probably a little under-recorded.

SILVER-SPOTTED SKIPPER *Hesperia comma* (Linn.)

Native. Formerly common in open grassland along the North Downs but declined dramatically during the 1960's. Now very rare and restricted to a single colony on downland at Lydden TR24S, but a casual record at South Alkham TR24K in 1990 could suggest that there are a few other as yet undiscovered colonies in the south-east of the county.

The larvae feed upon Sheep's-fescue *Festuca ovina* agg. during the spring and early summer and the adult butterfly is on the wing during August and the first few days of September.

LARGE SKIPPER   *Ochlodes venata* (Bremer & Grey)

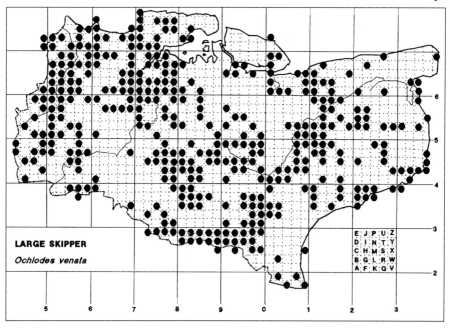

LARGE SKIPPER

Ochlodes venata

E	J	P	U	Z
D	I	N	T	Y
C	H	M	S	X
B	G	L	R	W
A	F	K	Q	V

Native. In open woodland, neglected gardens and parks, and in areas of open scrub; frequent in places but rather patchily distributed within the county. The over-wintering larvae feed upon broad-leaved grasses although there are no recent records from Kent of the actual species of grass.

The adult butterfly is best found during July but the extreme dates during the survey were 28th May and 17th August. There appears to have been little if any change of status this century within the county.

DINGY SKIPPER *Erynnis tages* (Linn.)

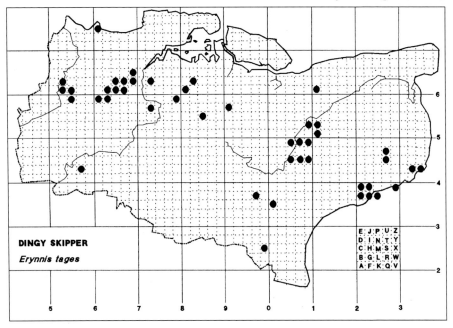

DINGY SKIPPER
Erynnis tages

E	J	P	U	Z
D	I	N	T	Y
C	H	M	S	X
B	G	L	R	W
A	F	K	Q	V

Native. Open downland and scrub on the chalk and occasionally in old quarries and open woodland elsewhere. The over-wintering larvae feed upon Common Bird's-foot-trefoil *Lotus corniculatus* with the resultant butterflies being recorded on the wing from the 2nd May until the l9th June. In the past an occasional second brood has been recorded in late August. Very little change of status in recent years.

GRIZZLED SKIPPER

Pyrgus malvae (Linn.)

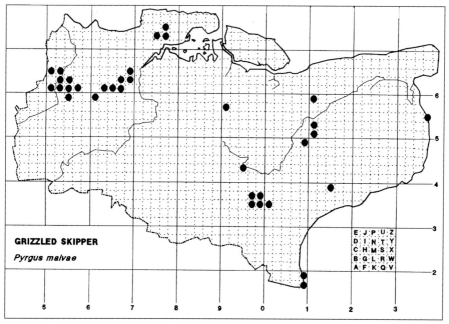

Native. On chalk downland, open woodland and areas of open scrub. Widely but thinly scattered in the county although quite frequent on the Downs between the Darent and the Medway. This insect over-winters as a pupa, with the adult butterflies recorded from 24th May until the 20th June. There is the very occasional partial second brood such as one recorded on Trottiscliffe (Trosley) Downs on 12th July 1989.

The larvae have been recorded feeding upon Wild Strawberry *Fragaria vesca* between late May and early July and they probably also feed upon other plants in the Rosaceae such as *Potentilla* spp. This species seems to have disappeared from some of its former localities but it is holding its own or increasing at others such as Dungeness where it was first recorded in 1976.

APOLLO   *Parnassius apollo* (Linn.)

Vagrant. Single specimens were captured at Dover in 1847 or 1848 and
again in 1889, at St. Margaret's Bay in 1898 and at Folkestone Warren in
1955. A single specimen seen flying in a garden at Loose TQ55L in
August 1986 was almost certainly an escape from captivity.

Sub family Papilioninae

SWALLOWTAIL   *Papilio machaon* (Linn.)

Scarce immigrant. This butterfly was first recorded in Kent in 1717, and
has been recorded irregularly since, sometimes many years passing
without a record, and then followed by a year or more when several
individuals were sighted. In some years these continental immigrants
have bred in the county, the usual foodplant being the foliage of the
Cultivated Carrot *Daucus carota* ssp. *sativus* with occasionally that of
Rue *Ruta graveolens*, Fennel *Foeniculum vulgare* or Pepper Saxifrage
Silaum silaus being used. This continental form is now known as ssp.
gorganus Fruhstorfer. During the course of this survey the only records
were of single specimens at Canterbury TR15P in August 1984, South
Foreland TR36L in August 1986 and Foreness Point TR37V in September

1986. Single specimens at Maidstone TQ75H in 1989 and TQ75R in 1990 were almost certainly escapes from captivity.

SCARCE SWALLOWTAIL   *Iphiclides podalirius* (Linn.)

Past records for this fine butterfly are probably or certainly escapes, or deliberate releases from captivity

Family PIERIDAE
Sub family Dismorphiinae

WOOD WHITE   *Leptidea sinapis* (Linn.)

Native resident, now extinct. Although formerly widespread in some of the Kentish woodlands, this butterfly was last recorded in the county in 1915 and has not been seen since.

Sub family Coliadinae

PALE CLOUDED YELLOW   *Colias hyale* (Linn.)

Irregular immigrant. First recorded in the county in 1795 and irregularly since, some years in abundance and breeding, the larvae having been recorded feeding upon Lucerne *Medicago sativa*. Not recorded during the present survey and the last Kentish record that I can trace is for 1973. Hopefully it will turn up again in the future.

BERGER'S CLOUDED YELLOW   *Colias alfacariensis* Berger

Scarce immigrant. Not recognised as a good species until 1945 and recorded in Kent from 1948 onwards. However, older specimens have been located in collections, the earliest having been collected at Folkestone in 1875. The larvae have been recorded feeding upon Horseshoe Vetch *Hippocrepis comosa*, this difference being a useful aid to the separation of this and the previous, very similar looking butterfly. Not recorded during the present survey and the last record that I can trace is from Dungeness in 1962.

CLOUDED YELLOW   *Colias croceus* (Geoffroy)

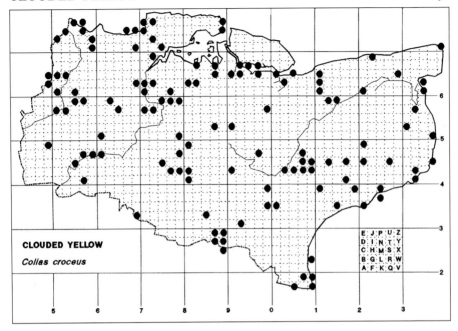

CLOUDED YELLOW

Colias croceus

Immigrant, occurring most years in small numbers with occasional blank years and with the odd year in great abundance. First recorded in Kent in 1717, there are many records of it breeding, the usual host plant being Lucerne *Medicago sativa* but Red Clover *Trifolium pratense* and White Clover *Trifolium repens* are regularly used as well. During the course of this survey there were no records for the years 1985 and 1988, but in 1983 there was a very large immigration and the butterfly probably occurred throughout the county. The adult butterfly was recorded on the wing between 8th June and the 6th November with peak numbers during August.

BRIMSTONE

Gonepteryx rhamni (Linn.)

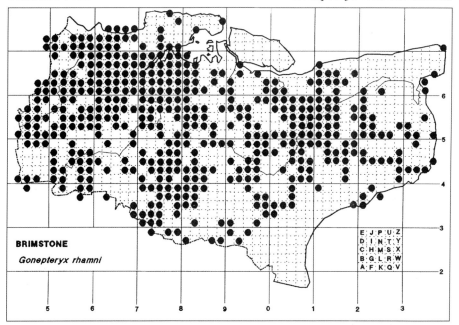

Native. In woods, commons, parks and gardens, frequent throughout most of the county although rare or absent from some coastal areas. The adult butterfly hibernates over the winter and has been recorded on the wing from February onwards. The larvae have been recorded feeding upon Buckthorn *Rhamnus catharticus* and Alder Buckthorn *Frangula alnus* but it is thought that other foodplants must be used at times as the butterfly is regularly recorded in some areas where neither of these plants occur. In July the occasional tattered specimen has been observed on the wing at the same time as the pristine new generation. The adult butterfly will usually enter into hibernation quite early but there are records of it on the wing until late into November. The status of this butterfly appears to have changed very little over recent years.

Sub family Coliadinae

CLEOPATRA   *Gonepteryx cleopatra* (Linn.)

Casual vagrant. Specimens recorded from Tunbridge Wells in 1916 were certainly escapes from captivity. However, a specimen observed at Temple Ewell TR24X in 1981 was probably genuinely wild, perhaps having crossed the Channel by ferry in a car or lorry.

Sub family Pierinae

BLACK-VEINED WHITE   *Aporia crataegi* (Linn.)

Native resident, now extinct in the British Isles. By 1885 this butterfly was restricted to an area of north-east Kent with the last positive record in 1922. Since then, any correctly claimed sighting can be accounted for by accidental or deliberate releases from captive stock. It now appears that the Black-veined White is unable to re-establish itself in this country.

LARGE WHITE   *Pieris brassicae* (Linn.)

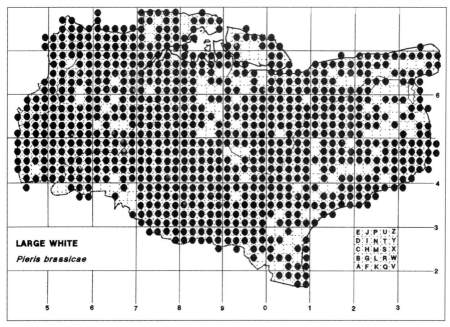

LARGE WHITE
Pieris brassicae

Native resident, its numbers regularly reinforced by immigration. Found throughout the county in all habitats but particularly about gardens and allotments. The larvae feed upon the leaves of Cabbage *Brassica oleracea* both the wild and cultivated varieties, particularly on Brussels-sprouts, but are also regularly found upon garden Nasturtium *Tropaeolum majus*.

The actual numbers of this butterfly vary quite considerably from year to year, depending upon the numbers of migrants that arrive and on the controlling effects of the braconid parasite *Apanteles glomeratus*. In favourable years it can become a pest in gardens and allotments as the larvae skeletonize the cabbage leaves, but in poor years the adults can be difficult to find and many gardens will not show a sign of the caterpillar.

The Large White overwinters in the pupal stage, with the adults usually emerging in late April. Two, and in warm years three, overlapping broods are produced, with adults being found on the wing throughout the summer. During the course of this survey the earliest record was for the 27th March and the latest on 10th October, with peak numbers during August.

SMALL WHITE
Pieris rapae (Linn.)

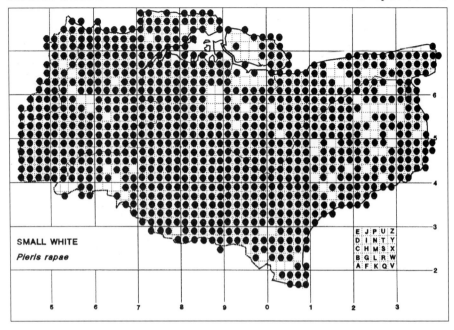

SMALL WHITE

Pieris rapae

Resident, but numbers reinforced by immigration in most years. A common, sometimes abundant species found throughout the county, the apparent gaps in its distribution probably being due to under-recording rather than absence of the butterfly. Although normally overwintering as a pupa there have been occasional early records of the adult butterfly from inside buildings such as greenhouses. In the open it has been recorded flying from as early as the 29th March and until the 23rd October, with peak numbers during July and August.

The larvae were recorded feeding upon cabbage *Brassica oleracea* and other garden brassicas. They probably also feed upon other wild species of the Brassicaceae. Records show that there are two and sometimes three broods per year.

GREEN-VEINED WHITE

Pieris napi (Linn.)

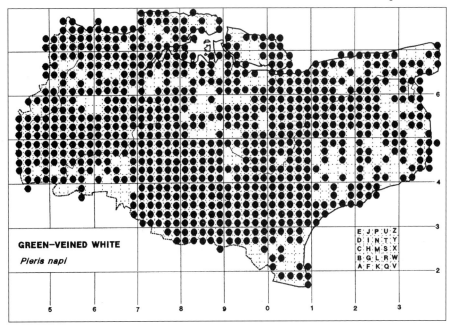

Resident, but with the numbers occasionally reinforced by immigration. A common species, found throughout the county in gardens, parks, woods, marshes and roadsides in all but the most built-up areas. It overwinters as a pupa. The adult butterfly was recorded on the wing from 9th April until 28th September with two overlapping broods peaking in May-June and July-August. The larvae have been recorded feeding upon Cuckooflower *Cardamine pratensis* and Garlic Mustard *Alliaria petiolata* and will probably also feed upon other wild species of Brassicaceae at times.

BATH WHITE

Pontia daplidice (Linn.)

Scarce immigrant, not recorded during this survey. First recorded in the county in 1818, there has been a scattering of records at intervals since, the last in 1950 when five specimens were observed.

ORANGE-TIP   *Anthocharis cardamines* (Linn.)

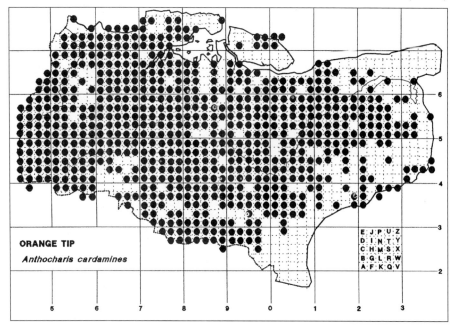

ORANGE TIP

Anthocharis cardamines

Native. Woods, gardens, field-borders and vegetated roadsides. Common throughout most of the county but scarce or absent from the coastal marshland areas. Usually single-brooded. This species overwinters as a pupa with the adult butterfly having been recorded on the wing from 1st April until the 17th June, with peak numbers during May. A few records of adults on the wing in the July of 1989 and 1990 suggested a partial second brood during these rather warm years. The larvae have been recorded feeding upon Cuckooflower *Cardamine pratensis* and Garlic Mustard *Alliaria petiolata* and in gardens upon Dame's-violet *Hesperis matronalis* and Honesty *Lunaria annua*.

DAPPLED WHITE   *Euchloe simplonia* (Freyer)

Two specimens caught on Castle Heights, Dover in August 1887 may have been genuine immigrants.

GREEN HAIRSTREAK

Callophrys rubi (Linn.)

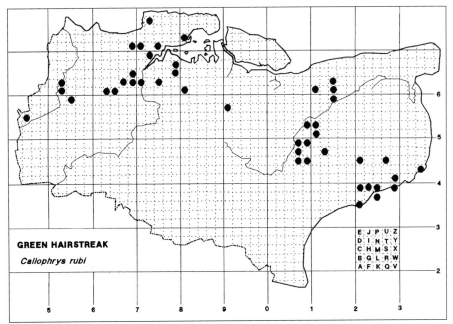

GREEN HAIRSTREAK

Callophrys rubi

Native. In open woodland, downland and areas of scrub, particularly on the chalk. Scattered colonies but never abundant, although regularly found at the same sites each year. This species of Hairstreak overwinters as a pupa, with the adult on the wing during May and June. The extreme dates for the imago during this survey were 28th April and 7th July. The larvae have been observed feeding upon Common Rock-rose *Helianthemum nummularium*, Dogwood *Cornus sanguinea*, Broom *Cytisus scoparius*, Bramble *Rubus fruticosus* agg. and Common Bird's-foot Trefoil *Lotus corniculatus* and there are records of many other food plants. The larvae feed up quickly and about nine months are spent in the pupal stage.

BROWN HAIRSTREAK

Thecla betulae (Linn.)

Native, but now probably extinct in Kent. Formerly widely distributed this butterfly has not been recorded in the county since 1971 in spite of repeated searches in some of its former habitats.

23

PURPLE HAIRSTREAK

Quercusia quercus (Linn.)

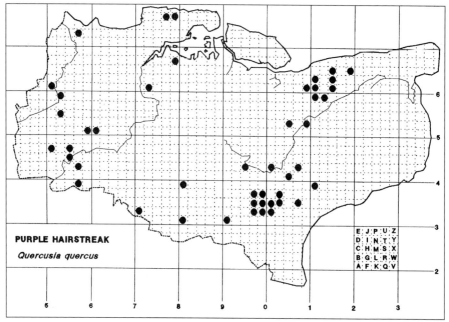

PURPLE HAIRSTREAK

Quercusia quercus

Native. In woods, parkland and hedgerows provided that oak trees are present. This butterfly is widely distributed but never abundant in Kent, its colonies often overlooked because adults spend a significant proportion of their lives confined to the tree canopy. Overwinters in the egg stage; the resultant larvae have been observed during April and May feeding upon *Quercus robur* and will probably feed upon other species of oak as well. The adult was recorded on the wing between 14th June and 6th September with peak numbers during late July and early August.

WHITE-LETTER HAIRSTREAK *Satyrium w-album* (Knoch)

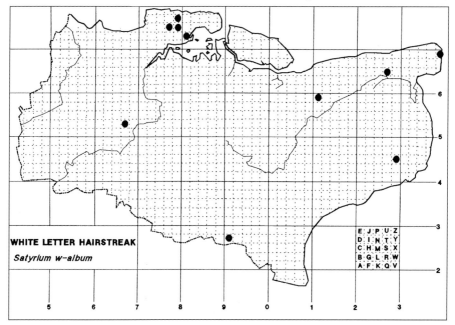

WHITE LETTER HAIRSTREAK
Satyrium w-album

Native. Woodland borders and hedgerows that contain elm. Now rather scarce but formerly much more frequent and widespread, its demise probably due to the loss of its food plant through Dutch Elm Disease. The adult butterfly has a relatively short flight period and has been recorded on the wing between 6th July and 16th August.

The larvae emerge in April from overwintering eggs and feed upon the leaves of Wych Elm *Ulmus glabra* and occasionally English Elm *Ulmus procera*, usually as good standing trees, but in recent years some larvae have been noted on elm suckers.

SMALL COPPER   *Lycaena phlaeas* (Linn.)

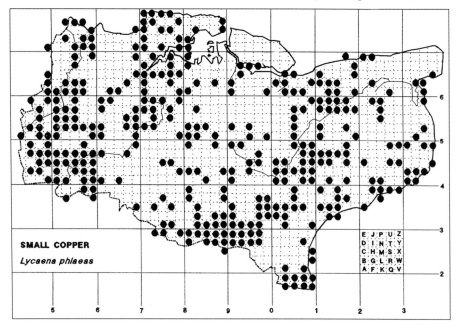

SMALL COPPER

Lycaena phlaeas

E	J	P	U	Z
D	I	N	T	Y
C	H	M	S	X
B	G	L	R	W
A	F	K	Q	V

Native. Heathland, downland, sand dunes, woodland clearings and rough open grassy areas. Scattered throughout most of the county but absent apparently from some areas, the actual numbers varying very much from season to season. Larvae have been found feeding upon Sheep's Sorrel *Rumex acetosella* although in captivity they will eat any species of *Rumex* offered to them. This species overwinters in the larval state and the adult butterfly appears then to be continuously brooded throughout the summer months provided the temperature is warm enough, and has been recorded on the wing from 30th April until 31st October.

LARGE COPPER   *Lycaena dispar* (Haworth)
A few very old doubtful records and unlikely to occur now.

PURPLE-EDGED COPPER   *Lycaena hippothoe* (Linn.)
One very old record with doubtful credentials.

Sub family Polyommatinae

LONG-TAILED BLUE   *Lampides boeticus* (Linn.)
Rare immigrant. About 25 records over the years, the last being for a single specimen at Folkestone in 1957.

Sub family Polyommatinae

SMALL BLUE   *Cupido minimus* (Fuessly)

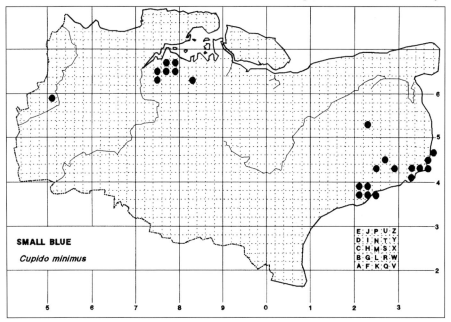

SMALL BLUE

Cupido minimus

E	J	P	U	Z
D	I	N	T	Y
C	H	M	S	X
B	G	L	R	W
A	F	K	Q	V

Native. Downland and rough grassy areas on the chalk. Very local, usually occurring in small colonies and rather elusive unless especially looked for. The adult butterfly has been observed on the wing from 25th May through to 19th July with peak numbers in June. In warm years there may be a partial second brood with adults being recorded from 6th until 31st August. The larvae overwinter and in summer feed exclusively on Kidney Vetch *Anthyllis vulneraria* which is one of the reasons for the restricted distribution of this dainty little butterfly.

SHORT-TAILED BLUE   *Everes argiades* (Pallas)
A very rare immigrant of which there is only one very old doubtful record.

SILVER-STUDDED BLUE   *Plebejus argus* (Linn.)
Native, but now probably extinct in the county. Formerly there were a number of colonies, mainly on the chalk, throughout the county, but there was a marked decline in numbers from about 1949 with the last positive sighting in 1966. There have been a few odd unconfirmed reports since and there is just a chance, more in hope than scientific judgement, that this butterfly might still be lingering on in Kent.

BROWN ARGUS   *Aricia agestis* (Denis & Schiff.)

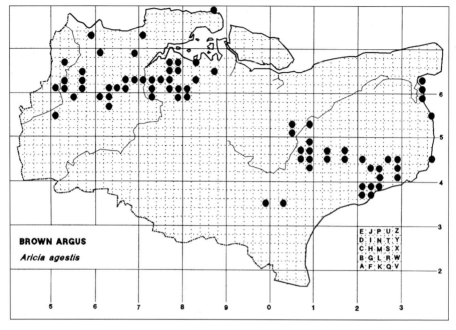

Native. Scattered colonies throughout the county, mainly on the chalk but not always as it is regularly recorded from Orlestone Forest and Sandwich Bay areas. Although never abundant the numbers appear reasonably constant from year to year. There are two broods per year with the adult butterflies recorded on the wing from 15th May until 30th June and from 17th July until 10th September.

The larvae have been observed feeding upon Common Rock-rose *Helianthemum nummularium* and probably feed upon various species of Crane's-bill *Geranium* spp. and Stork's-bill *Erodium* spp. as well. This species over-winters in the larval stage.

COMMON BLUE   *Polyommatus icarus* (Rott.)

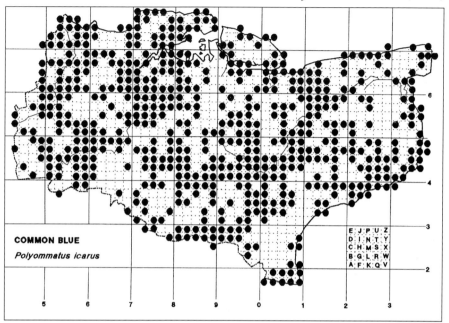

COMMON BLUE

Polyommatus icarus

Native. Open downland, meadows, roadside verges and neglected areas of grassland or scrub. Scattered throughout the county, the actual numbers appear to have declined in recent years although the adult butterfly is still likely to be found in any suitable habitat. The overwintering larvae go into hibernation in late September or early October and begin to feed again in late March or early April. They have been recorded feeding upon Common Bird's-foot Trefoil *Lotus corniculatus* and almost certainly feed upon other species of Bird's-foot-trefoil *Lotus* spp., Medick *Medicago* spp. and Clover *Trifolium* spp.

The adult butterfly is on the wing during mid-May to June with the second brood flying during July and August and into September. Some of these September specimens might represent a partial third brood but it is difficult to be sure of this in the field as adult butterflies were recorded throughout the summer months from 24th April until 8th October.

CHALK HILL BLUE   *Lysandra coridon* (Poda)

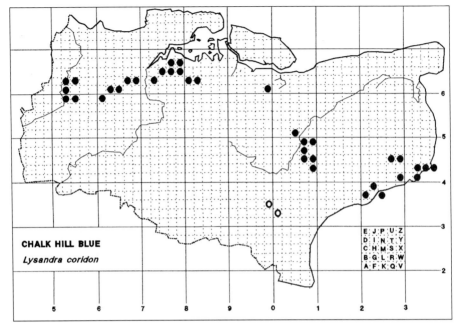

Native, in grassy areas on the chalk. Although still quite numerous in some of its colonies the distribution of the Chalk Hill Blue in the county has been greatly reduced in recent years owing to the loss of habitat, either through ploughing or scrub invasion. The adult butterfly is mainly on the wing during August and has been recorded from 22nd July until 12th September. Over-wintering in the egg stage, the resultant larvae emerge in late April and feed upon Horseshoe Vetch *Hippocrepis comosa*. The restricted distribution of the foodplant (see p32) limits the range of this species in Kent, but the adults will wander at times as must have been the case of those specimens seen in the Orlestone Forest - Ham Street areas in 1989 and 1990.

ADONIS BLUE

Lysandra bellargus (Rott.)

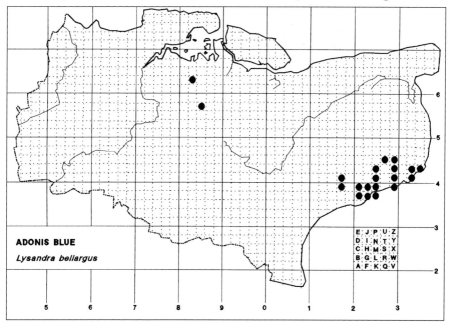

ADONIS BLUE

Lysandra bellargus

Native. On downland and rough grassy areas on the chalk. Often in the same localities as the Chalk Hill Blue but much less frequent and with no recent records from the west of the county. This species overwinters in the larval stage and resumes feeding in mid or late March. The caterpillar feeds exclusively on Horseshoe Vetch *Hippocrepis comosa* and in captivity will accept nothing else.

There are two broods per year with the adult butterfly on the wing in June (recorded from 27th May until 29th June) and in the second half of August (recorded from 31st July until 13th September). The range of the Adonis Blue, like that of the previous species, is very much restricted by the presence of the food plant.

HORSESHOE VETCH   *Hippocrepis comosa* L.

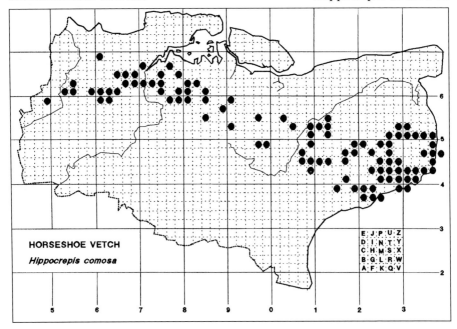

HORSESHOE VETCH
Hippocrepis comosa

This map shows the present known distribution of Horseshoe Vetch which as the larval food plant of the Adonis Blue and the Chalk Hill Blue also represents the maximum potential distribution of these two butterflies in Kent.

Sub family Polyommatinae

TURQUOISE BLUE   *Plebicula dorylas* (Denis & Schiff.)
A few old records probably refer to errors in recording or identification.

MAZARINE BLUE   *Cyaniris semiargus* (Rott.)
A few old records, some of which are probably genuine, but not now recorded in the county for at least eighty years.

LARGE BLUE   *Maculinea arion* (Linn.)
There are somewhat doubtful claims that this species used to occur in the Folkestone-Deal area up until about 1828. The only other record is of one well-seen by a competent observer at Queendown Warren in 1976, although it is difficult to explain this record.

HOLLY BLUE   *Celastrina argiolus* (Linn.)

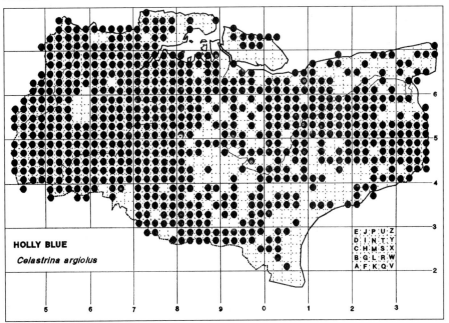

HOLLY BLUE

Celastrina argiolus

Native. In parks, gardens, churchyards, borders of woods, hedgerows and isolated areas of scrub with a few trees. At the start of this survey this butterfly had reached a rather low ebb and only two records for the whole of the county were received for 1981. For each subsequent year it showed a steady improvement in numbers and with a massive increase in 1989 and 1990 it was by then probably occurring in every tetrad within the county. There are normally two broods, and in warm years three per year, but in the recent warm years it has been impossible to differentiate the separate broods and the Holly Blue has appeared to be continuously brooded occurring on the wing from 12th March until the 13th October without a break. Traditionally the larva was known to feed upon Holly *Ilex aquifolium*, Ivy *Hedera helix* and sometimes Dogwood *Cornus sanguinea*, but during this population explosion it has appeared much more catholic and has been recorded feeding upon various species of Dogwood *Cornus* spp., Cotoneaster *Cotoneaster* spp., Buckthorn *Rhamnus* spp., Alder Buckthorn *Frangula alnus*, Firethorn *Pyracantha* spp. and other genera of shrubs, particularly on cultivated species. The Holly Blue over-winters in the pupal stage.

Grizzled Skipper (p13)

Brimstone (p17)

PLATE 1

Holly Blue (p33)

Green Hairstreak (p23)

PLATE 2

DUKE OF BURGUNDY FRITILLARY   *Hamearis lucina* (Linn.)

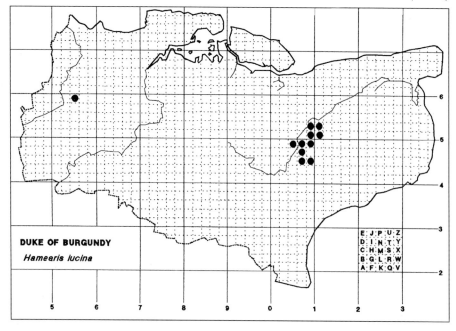

DUKE OF BURGUNDY
Hamearis lucina

E	J	P	U	Z
D	I	N	T	Y
C	H	M	S	X
B	G	L	R	W
A	F	K	Q	V

Native. Wood borders, woodland rides and open woodland. Although formerly much more widely distributed this species now appears to be restricted to the Wye-Crundale-Denge Wood area of the county. The 1988 record from Kemsing in West Kent is almost certainly of a deliberately liberated specimen and the species has not been recorded there since. The adult butterfly was recorded on the wing from 5th May until 16th June with peak numbers during the last week in May.

The larvae have been recorded feeding upon both Primrose *Primula vulgaris* and Cowslip *Primula veris* and the species overwinters from August onwards in the pupal stage. The subfamily Riodininae to which the Duke of Burgundy Fritillary belongs was formerly placed in the family Nemeobiidae but latest opinion places it in with the Blue butterflies in the family Lycaenidae.

WHITE ADMIRAL
Ladoga camilla (Linn.)

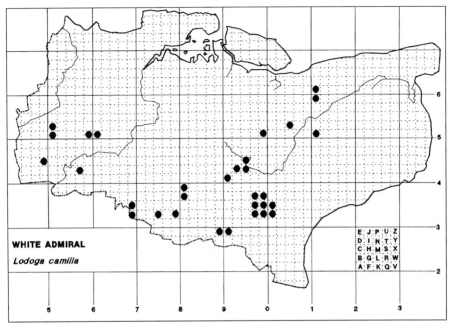

Native. In woodlands. This fine butterfly has fluctuated considerably in both range and numbers over the years and continues to do so. During the 1960's and 1970's this species was at a rather low ebb and was restricted to a few woods in the Weald. During the course of this survey the White Admiral has shown a steady expansion of range and although still only common in the Ham Street - Orlestone Forest area there is now a chance that odd specimens could turn up in any of the remaining major woodlands in the county.

The larvae overwinter in a hibernaculum constructed from a leaf of its foodplant Honeysuckle *Lonicera periclymenum* and do not commence feeding again until early or mid-April. The adult butterfly was recorded on the wing from 20th June until 16th August with a peak during July.

Purple Hairstreak (p24)

White-letter Hairstreak (p25)

PLATE 3

White Admiral (p35)

Peacock (p41)

PLATE 4

PURPLE EMPEROR
Apatura iris (Linn.)

Native. The Purple Emperor was formerly widespread and locally common in the county but from about 1850 there has been a steady decline so that a hundred years later it was virtually extinct. There were single records in the Orlestone Forest area in 1962 and 1967 but it was not recorded at all during the 1970's. During the present survey it has been recorded in the Tunbridge Wells - Penshurst area, once in 1984 and two records in 1987. These, together with some non-proven records and records in 1991, suggest that this grand butterfly could be established in very low numbers in the south west of the county in areas close to the Sussex border.

RED ADMIRAL   *Vanessa atalanta* (Linn.)

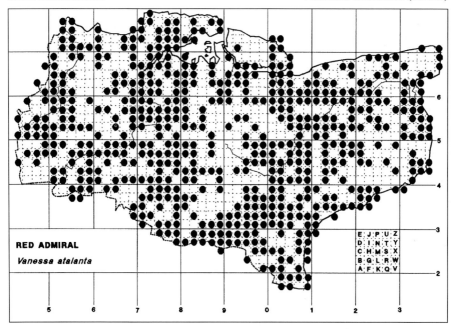

RED ADMIRAL

Vanessa atalanta

E	J	P	U	Z
D	I	N	T	Y
C	H	M	S	X
B	Q	L	R	W
A	F	K	Q	V

This fine butterfly is found throughout the county. It is regularly found in gardens but is likely to occur in any habitat provided a food source in the form of flowers, either wild or cultivated, is to be found. The adults have also been recorded feeding upon ripe fruits such as apples or blackberries and also upon sap runs from injured tree trunks. The numbers are maintained by immigration most years and the strength of this immigration, which can extend from April through to July, will determine the numbers of butterflies to be seen each year. The adults have been recorded throughout the year with peak numbers from the end of April until early October with some suggestions of a partial southward migration in some years from late August until November. In recent years at least, some specimens have overwintered, but this is more of a resting up in very cold weather rather than true hibernation. The larvae have been recorded feeding upon Common Nettle *Urtica dioica* and Hop *Humulus lupulus*, and have been found throughout the summer months, but it is difficult to say if this is the breeding of successive waves of immigrants or of an actual second brood.

Heath Fritillary (p47)

Heath Fritillary (underside) (p47)

PLATE 5

Pearl-bordered Fritillary (p43)

Silver-washed Fritillary (p46)

PLATE 6

PAINTED LADY   *Cynthia cardui* (Linn.)

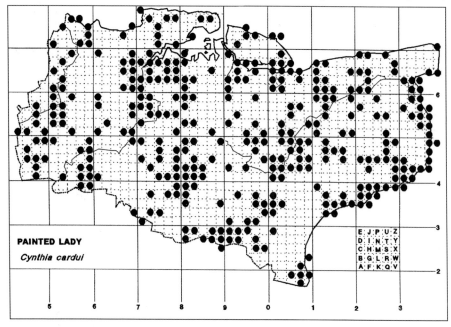

PAINTED LADY

Cynthia cardui

E	J	P	U	Z
D	I	N	T	Y
C	H	M	S	X
B	G	L	R	W
A	F	K	Q	V

Immigrant. Gardens, parks, hedgerows and flowery waste places, particularly near the coast. Recorded every year of the survey, the numbers depending upon the strength of the immigration. 1981 was a very poor year but in 1982, 1985, 1988 and 1990 the Painted Lady was to be found in very large numbers across the county. Adults were recorded on the wing from 4th April until 19th October with peak numbers during August. There was one exceptionally late specimen seen at East Malling on 23rd December 1987. Larvae were recorded most years soon after the first immigrants had arrived and were observed feeding upon Spear Thistle *Cirsium vulgare* and Creeping Thistle *Cirsium arvense*.

AMERICAN PAINTED LADY   *Cynthia virginiensis* (Dury)

Rare vagrant. The only record for the county is of a specimen taken at Dover in 1886, although there is some doubt as to the history of this specimen.

SMALL TORTOISESHELL

Aglais urticae (Linn.)

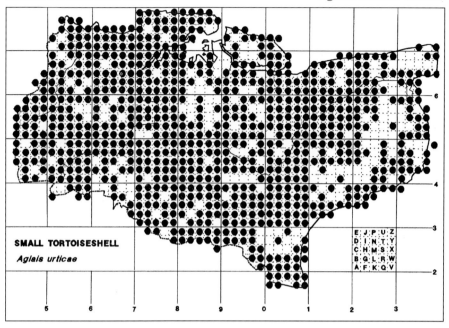

SMALL TORTOISESHELL

Aglais urticae

Resident, although on rare occasions its numbers can be supplemented by immigrants. Common throughout the county and in all probability will occur in every tetrad in Kent. However, at times there can be some fluctuation in status of this butterfly, and from about halfway through the present survey there was a steep decline in numbers. So much so that many recorders during 1989 and 1990 were commenting on the absence of this species rather than being able to find new records and this is partly the reason for some large gaps in the distribution map. In 1991 however, there was a considerable increase in numbers although not back to its former abundance.

The adult butterfly was recorded throughout the year but with few records during the months of December, January and February when those seen would have been of specimens disturbed from hibernation. There are two broods per year and all records of larvae were of specimens feeding upon Common Nettle *Urtica dioica*.

Speckled Wood (p48)

Wall (p49)

PLATE 7

Gatekeeper (p52)

Meadow Brown (p53)

PLATE 8

Sub family Nymphalinae

LARGE TORTOISESHELL   *Nymphalis polychloros* (Linn.)

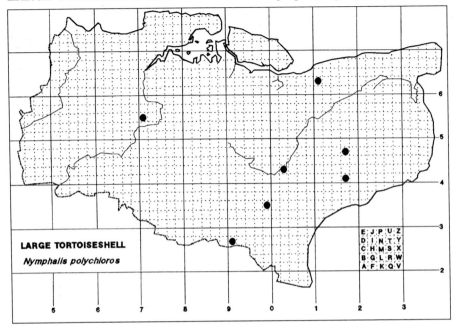

LARGE TORTOISESHELL
Nymphalis polychloros

Scarce immigrant and occasional temporary resident. The few records during the survey are all of single specimens save for the records from Barming TQ75C when several specimens and larvae feeding upon English Elm *Ulmus procera* were observed during 1984.

SCARCE TORTOISESHELL   *Nymphalis xanthomelas* (Denis & Schiff.)

The only British record is of one caught at Shipborne on 2nd July 1953.

CAMBERWELL BEAUTY   *Nymphalis antiopa* (Linn.)

Irregular immigrant. The history of this butterfly is well documented by Chalmers-Hunt in his *Butterflies and Moths of Kent* 1960-1981. The last time that this species occurred in the county in any numbers was in 1976 with two further records in 1978. The only record during this survey was of one observed in the National Nature Reserve at Ham Street TR03B on 15th May 1990.

PEACOCK

Inachis io (Linn.)

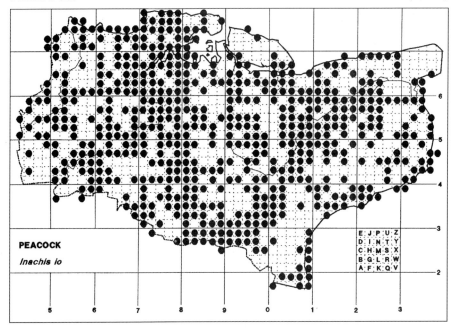

PEACOCK

Inachis io

Resident. Found throughout the county particularly in gardens, parks, hedgerows and about farmsteads. Usually rather common but it became much less frequent during the last three years of the survey. There was however, a great resurgence in numbers in 1991.

The adult butterfly was recorded in every month of the year, although the few records during December, January and February were either of hibernating individuals or of those disturbed from hibernation. There are also few records during the month of June and these are either of very worn specimens or of early, freshly emerged specimens in some of the very warm years. Larvae, feeding upon Common Nettle *Urtica dioica* were recorded during June and July.

41

COMMA   *Polygonia c-album* (Linn.)

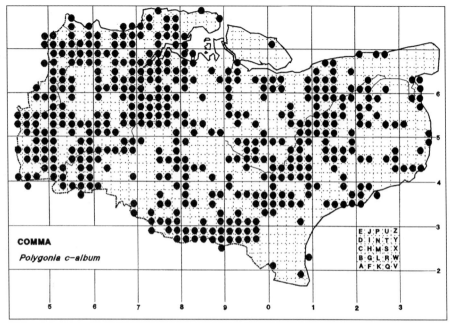

COMMA
Polygonia c-album

Resident. Up until about 1932 this butterfly was rather scarce and of
irregular appearance, but since that date there has been a steady
increase in both its range and numbers so that by now the Comma is a
common and regular butterfly throughout the county. This steady
increase in numbers still appears to be continuing. The adult butterfly
has been recorded on the wing from 4th March until 25th October, with
the occasional hibernating specimen disturbed during the months
November to February. There appear to be two broods per year and the
larvae have been recorded feeding upon Common Nettle *Urtica dioica*
and Hop *Humulus lupulus*.

Sub family Argynninae

SMALL PEARL-BORDERED FRITILLARY
                                    Boloria selene (Denis & Schiff.)
Native. Formerly widespread although never common. This butterfly, in
common with the other species of fritillary, has shown a marked decrease
in both range and numbers in recent years and the only record during the
present survey was of one small colony in the Orlestone Forest area TQ93.

PEARL-BORDERED FRITILLARY *Boloria euphrosyne* (Linn.)

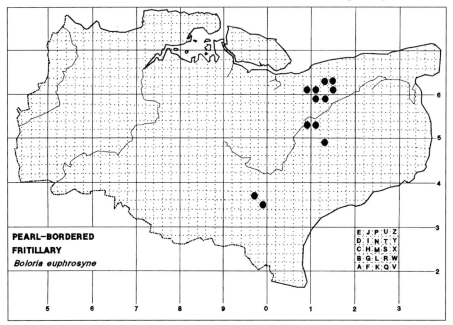

PEARL-BORDERED
FRITILLARY
Boloria euphrosyne

Native. Formerly widespread and quite common in most of the woods in Kent this species now appears to be restricted to the Orlestone Forest area and the woods that encircle Canterbury. The adult butterfly has been recorded on the wing from 6th May until well into June with peak numbers during the last week in May. This species over-winters in the larval stage and has been recorded feeding upon Common Dog-violet *Viola riviniana*.

WEAVER'S FRITILLARY *Boloria dia* (Linn.)

There is a doubtful record of two specimens taken at Southborough in 1873.

QUEEN OF SPAIN FRITILLARY *Argynnis lathonia* (Linn.)

Rare immigrant. The only record during the survey was of one seen at East Sutton TQ84J on 9th August 1987.

NIOBE FRITILLARY *Argynnis niobe* (Linn.)

A few doubtful records from last century, the last from Deal in 1892.

HIGH BROWN FRITILLARY *Argynnis adippe* (Denis & Schiff.)

Native, now extinct in the county. Formerly quite widespread in wooded areas in Kent but has decreased quite seriously since the last war. The last record is of a single specimen caught and released in Hoads Wood in 1971.

DARK GREEN FRITILLARY   *Argynnis aglaja* (Linn.)

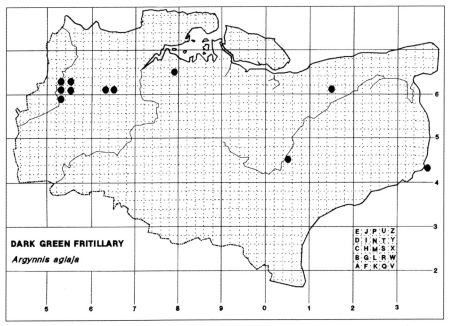

DARK GREEN FRITILLARY

Argynnis aglaja

Native. Chalk downland and open woods. Formerly widespread throughout most of the county but in line with most other fritillaries its numbers have declined quite seriously in recent years and it is now restricted to a very few sites, with the only regular sites being along the chalk downs between the Darent and Medway valleys. The adult butterfly has been recorded on the wing from 24th June until 21st August. The larvae have been observed feeding upon a species of Violet *Viola* spp.

45

SILVER-WASHED FRITILLARY — *Argynnis paphia* (Linn.)

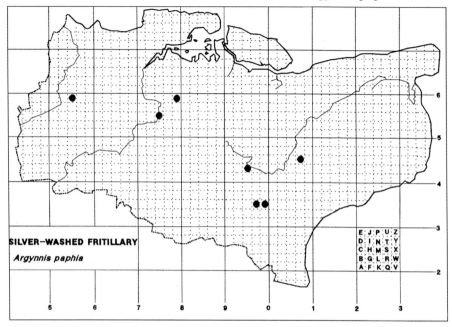

SILVER-WASHED FRITILLARY

Argynnis paphia

E	J	P	U	Z
D	I	N	T	Y
C	H	M	S	X
B	G	L	R	W
A	F	K	Q	V

Native. Formerly frequent in just about every oak wood in the county this fine butterfly is now on the verge of becoming extinct as a Kentish species. The accompanying map shows all the localities where this species has been recorded during the present survey. Apart from fairly regular sightings in the Orlestone Forest area and rather more casual records at Kemsing the other sightings refer to 1984 when a number of specimens was seen, mainly males, perhaps as a result of dispersal from a neighbouring county. Adult butterflies have been recorded on the wing from the 12th July until the end of August.

Sub family Melitaeinae

MARSH FRITILLARY — *Eurodryas aurinia* (Rott.)

Native, but now extinct in the county. There are old records from several localities in Kent the main one being Ham Fen (TR35H) where it was last seen toward the end of the last war in 1945.

GLANVILLE FRITILLARY — *Melitaea cinxia* (Linn.)

Native, but now long extinct. Formerly in the Folkestone-Dover area but not seen there this century.

HEATH FRITILLARY   *Mellicta athalia* (Rott.)

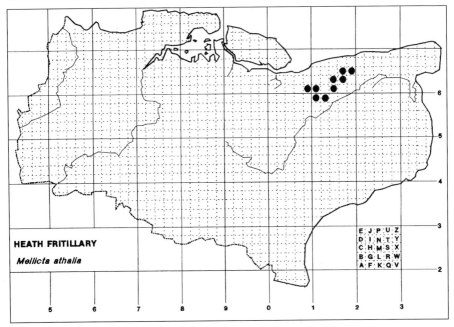

HEATH FRITILLARY

Mellicta athalia

Native. Long established in the Blean Woods area and still flourishing there. This local butterfly is prone to fluctuations in its numbers and moves about the woods depending on the state of the coppicing. The bulk of the woodlands within the range of this species are now actively managed by English Nature, the Royal Society for the Protection of Birds or the Kent Trust for Nature Conservation and unless anything unforeseen happens then the future of this butterfly appears secure.

The adult butterfly has been recorded on the wing from the 10th June until the 29th July. The eggs are laid on any convenient leaf or branch, often on Bramble *Rubus* sp. The larvae are gregarious at first, but by the third instar usually feed solitarily. During winter they form a hibernaculum spun from dead leaves. The larvae have been observed feeding upon Common Cow-wheat *Melampyrum pratense* and probably also feed on other low plants such as Ribwort Plantain *Plantago lanceolata*. This species is scheduled as RDB 2 (species likely to be categorised as endangered or possibly extinct if their populations are depleted any further) and must not be collected or disturbed in any way.

Sub family Satyrinae

SPECKLED WOOD   *Pararge aegeria* (Linn.)

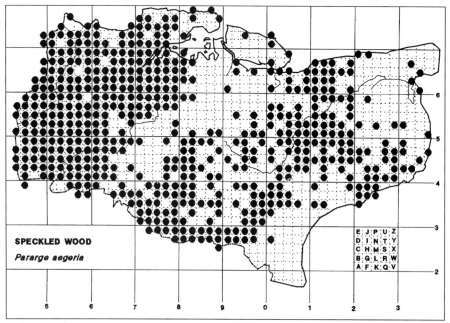

Resident. By the turn of the century this species had become quite local and its numbers continued to decline over subsequent years. A single specimen was taken at Chattenden in 1913 and the Speckled Wood was not recorded again in Kent until it turned up in the east of the county in 1942. Since then this species has spread throughout the county and is found in open woodland, copses, parks, gardens and lanesides and is now one of our most frequent butterflies.

The adult is on the wing during the summer months having been recorded from 17th March until 2nd November and is almost continuously brooded. The Speckled Wood over-winters in both the larval and pupal stages. The caterpillar has been observed feeding upon grasses in Kent, although the host species were not determined.

48

WALL   *Lasiommata megera* (Linn.)

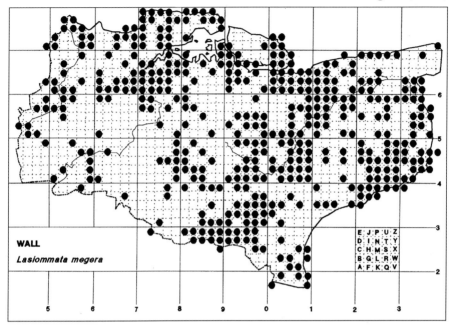

WALL

Lasiommata megera

Resident. Downland, parks, gardens, lanesides and open rough grassy areas. This species has been subject to periodic changes in numbers and distribution but at present it is found throughout the county being more frequent in coastal areas, but nowhere can it be said to be really common.

The adult butterfly was recorded on the wing from 21st April until 13th October with peaks in mid-May until mid-June and again during August. The Wall over-winters in the larval state and the caterpillar has been recorded feeding upon Cock's-foot grass *Dactylis glomerata*.

MARBLED WHITE   *Melanargia galathea* (Linn.)

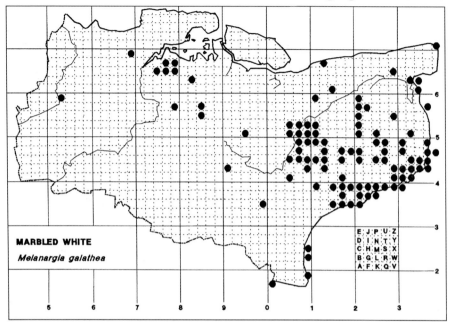

MARBLED WHITE

Melanargia galathea

Native. Chalk downland and open grassy area. Another species that is subject to considerable changes in its distribution over the years. In 1981 it was at a rather low ebb and was to be found in just a few isolated colonies in the east of the county. However during the course of this survey its numbers have shown a steady improvement each year and its range has been steadily spreading westward and the signs are that this expansion will continue.

The adult butterfly was recorded on the wing from 16th June until 29th August with peak numbers during July. The Marbled White over-winters in the larval state and the caterpillar has been observed feeding upon fine-leaved grasses.

GRAYLING   *Hipparchia semele* (Linn.)

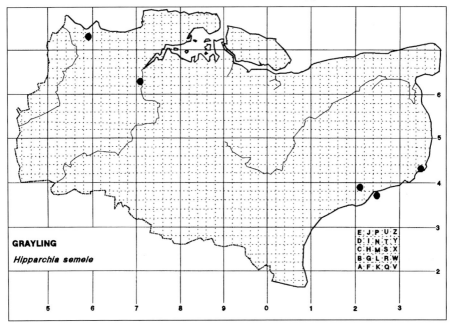

GRAYLING

Hipparchia semele

Native. Formerly common on most of the open chalk downland in the
county this species has shown a marked decrease in numbers since about
1960 and is now on the verge of becoming extinct in the county. There
appear to be a few struggling colonies in the Folkestone-Deal area, one
small colony near Swanscombe, with the only other possible colony being
in the Burham Downs area where the odd casual butterfly has been
recorded. The adult butterfly was recorded on the wing from 25th July
until the end of August.

GATEKEEPER *Pyronia tithonus* (Linn.)

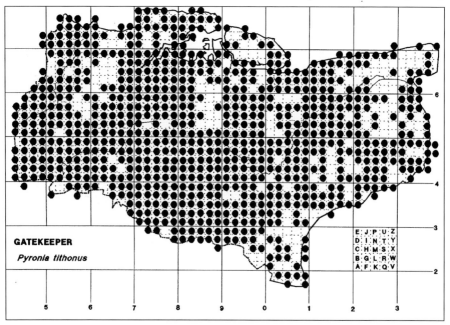

Native. Hedgerows, borders of woods and bushy areas. Widely distributed throughout the county and records suggest that this species has been increasing in both distribution and numbers over recent years. The eggs hatch during August and the larvae feed until late October when they enter a strict diapause. The larvae commence feeding again in early spring and have been observed eating various grasses. The adult butterfly has been recorded on the wing from 29th June until 11th September.

MEADOW BROWN   *Maniola jurtina* (Linn.)

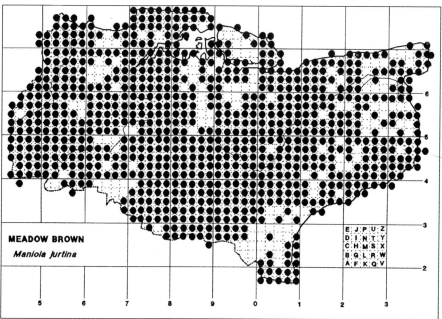

MEADOW BROWN

Maniola jurtina

E	J	P	U	Z
D	I	N	T	Y
C	H	M	S	X
B	G	L	R	W
A	F	K	Q	V

Native. Meadows, downland and grassy roadside verges; common and probably to be found in any rough grassy area throughout the county. The over-wintering larvae do not enter into a true diapause but will continue to feed on mild days. The larvae have been observed feeding upon various grasses and will probably take a great variety of species. There are continuous records of the adult butterfly from 7th June until 10th September which probably represent two or more broods.

RINGLET   *Aphantopus hyperantus* (Linn.)

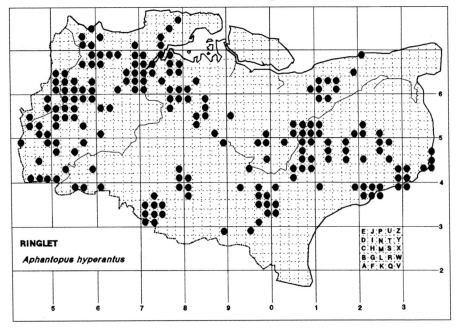

RINGLET

Aphantopus hyperantus

Native. Open woodlands, hedgerows and bushy places. Often found flying with the Meadow Brown although the Ringlet prefers to be in the vicinity of bushes and trees whilst the Meadow Brown has a preference for more open grassy areas. From ova laid in the summer months the larvae reach their third instar during October when they enter into partial hibernation, although they will continue to feed on mild days. The larvae feed upon various grasses, in captivity they will accept just about any species of grass but there are few positive records of which species are eaten in the wild. The adult butterfly was recorded on the wing from 9th June until 24th August with peak numbers during July.

SMALL HEATH   *Coenonympha pamphilus* (Linn.)

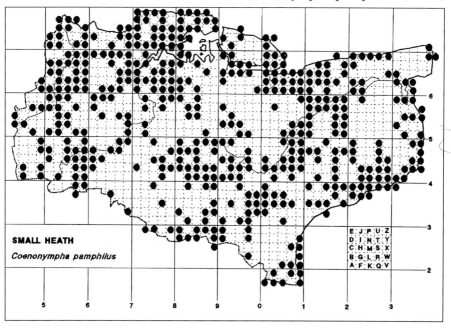

Native. Meadows, downland and grassy places generally. Found throughout the county except in heavily built-up or extensively cultivated areas, and although actual numbers appear to have declined in recent years it is still a fairly common butterfly. The larvae feed upon various grasses and during the winter months will go into a partial hiberation but will continue to feed on mild days. The adult butterfly was recorded on the wing from 5th May until 14th October.

Sub family Danainae

MILKWEED   *Danaus plexippus* (Linn.)

This rare transatlantic vagrant has been recorded a few times in the county, the last being in 1968.

INDEX

Previous Transactions of the
Kent Field Club include:

Vol 1   (3)   Kent Gall mites
          (4)   Kent leafhoppers and planthoppers
               Heteroptera of East Malling

Vol 2   Lepidoptera of Ashford district

Vol 3   (1)   Mammals of Kent
          (2)   Ants of Kent
               Kent Myxomycetes
          (3)   Hoverflies of Kent

Vol 4   Atlas of Kent Mosses

Vol 5   (2)   Kent slime-moulds (2)

Vol 7   Atlas of the seaweeds of Kent

Vol 8   (1)   Aphids of Kent
          (2)   Kent Charophytes

Vol 11 (1)   Bat hibernacula in Kent
          (2)   Atlas of the Newts of Kent

1982   Atlas of the Kent Flora

Forthcoming Atlases:
Orchids • Grasshoppers • Dragonflies • Bats